Essential Fic

Anthology

COMPILED BY

Brian Moses

Heinemann

Contents

Cider with Rosie

LAURIE LEE

Four-year-old Laurie lives with his mother and sisters in a tiny village. One day he is told he has to go to school.

The morning came, without any warning, when my sisters surrounded me, wrapped me in scarves, tied up my bootlaces, thrust a cap on my head, and stuffed a baked potato in my pocket.

'What's this?' I said.

'You're starting school today.'

'I ain't. I'm stopping 'ome.'

'Now, come on, Loll. You're a big boy now.'

'I ain't.'

'You are.'

'Boo-hoo.'

They picked me up bodily, kicking and bawling, and carried me up to the road.

'Boys who don't go to school get put into boxes, and turn into rabbits, and get chopped up Sundays.'

I felt this was overdoing it rather, but I said no more after that. I arrived at the school just three feet tall and fatly wrapped in my scarves. The playground roared like a rodeo, and the potato burned through my thigh. Old boots, ragged stockings, torn trousers and skirts, went skating and skidding around me. The rabble closed in; I was encircled; grit flew in my face like shrapnel. Tall girls with frizzled hair, and huge boys with sharp elbows, began to prod me with hideous interest. They plucked at my scarves, spun me round like a top, screwed my nose, and stole my potato.

I was rescued at last by a gracious lady – the sixteen-year-old junior-teacher – who boxed a few ears and dried my face and led me off to The Infants. I spent that first day picking holes in paper, then went home in a smouldering temper.

'What's the matter, Loll? Didn't he like it at school, then?'
'They never gave me the present!'
'Present? What present?'
'They said they'd give me a present.'
'Well, now, I'm sure they didn't.'
'They did! They said: "You're Laurie Lee, ain't you? Well, just you sit there for the present." I sat there all day but I never got it. I ain't going back there again!'

Illustrated by Victor G. Ambrus

Matilda

Roald Dahl

Matilda is five and a half and it's her first day at school.

Naturally Matilda was put in the bottom class, where there were eighteen other small boys and girls about the same age as her. Their teacher was called Miss Honey, and she could not have been more than twenty-three or twenty-four. She had a lovely pale oval madonna face with blue eyes and her hair was light-brown. Her body was so slim and fragile one got the feeling that if she fell over she would smash into a thousand pieces, like a porcelain figure.

Miss Jennifer Honey was a mild and quiet person who never raised her voice and was seldom seen to smile, but there is no doubt she possessed that rare gift for being adored by every small child under her care. She seemed to understand totally the bewilderment and fear that so often overwhelms young children who for the first time in their lives are herded into a classroom and told to obey orders. Some curious warmth that was almost tangible shone out of Miss Honey's face when she spoke to a confused and homesick newcomer to the class.

Miss Trunchbull, the Headmistress, was something else altogether. She was a gigantic holy terror, a fierce tyrannical monster who frightened the life out of the pupils and teachers alike. There was an aura of menace about her even at a distance, and when she came up close you could almost feel the dangerous heat radiating from her as from a red-hot rod of metal. When she marched – Miss Trunchbull never walked, she always marched like a storm-trooper with long strides and arms aswinging – when she marched along a corridor you could actually hear her snorting as she went, and if a group of children happened to be in her path, she ploughed right on through them like a tank, with small people bouncing off her to left and right. Thank goodness we don't meet many people like her in this world, although

they do exist and all of us are likely to come across at least one of them in a lifetime. If you ever do, you should behave as you would if you met an enraged rhinoceros out in the bush – climb up the nearest tree and stay there until it has gone away. This woman, in all her eccentricities and in her appearance, is almost impossible to describe, but I shall make some attempt to do so a little later on. Let us leave her for the moment and go back to Matilda and her first day in Miss Honey's class.

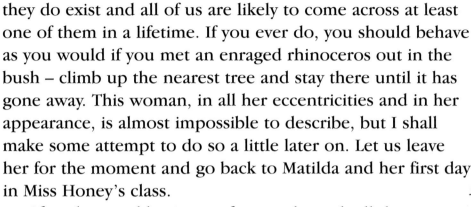

After the usual business of going through all the names of the children, Miss Honey handed out a brand-new exercise-book to each pupil.

"You have all brought you own pencils, I hope," she said.

"Yes, Miss Honey," they chanted.

"Good. Now this is the very first day of school for each one of you. It is the beginning of at least eleven long years of schooling that all of you are going to have to go through. And six of those years will be spent right here at Crunchem Hall where, as you know, your Headmistress is Miss Trunchbull. Let me for your own good tell you something about Miss Trunchbull. She insists upon strict discipline throughout the school, and if you take my advice you will do your very best to behave yourselves in her presence. Never argue with her. Never answer her back. Always do as she says. If you get on the wrong side of Miss Trunchbull she can liquidise you like a carrot in a kitchen blender. It's nothing to laugh about, Lavender. Take that grin off your face. All of you will be wise to remember that Miss Trunchbull deals very very severely with anyone who gets out of line in this school. Have you got the message?"

"Yes, Miss Honey," chirruped eighteen eager little voices.

Illustrated by Tony Ross

Oliver Twist

CHARLES DICKENS

The room in which the boys were fed was a large stone hall, with a copper at one end, out of which the master, dressed in an apron for the purpose, and assisted by one or two women, ladled the gruel at meal-times; of which composition each boy had one porringer, and no more – except on festive occasions, and then he had two ounces and a quarter of bread besides. The bowls never wanted washing. The boys polished them with their spoons till they shone again; and when they had performed this operation

10 (which never took very long, the spoons being nearly as large as the bowls), they would sit staring at the copper with such eager eyes as if they could have devoured the very bricks of which it was composed; employing themselves, meanwhile, in sucking their fingers most assiduously, with the view of catching up any stray splashes of gruel that might have been cast thereon. Boys have generally excellent appetites. Oliver Twist and his companions suffered the tortures of slow starvation for three months: at last they got so voracious and wild with

20 hunger, that one boy, who was tall for his age, and hadn't been used to that sort of thing (for his father had kept a small cookshop), hinted darkly to his companions, that unless he had another basin of gruel *per diem*, he was afraid he might some night happen to eat the boy who slept next to him, who happened to be a weakly youth of tender age. He had a wild, hungry eye; and they implicitly believed him. A council was held; lots were cast who should walk up to the master after supper that evening, and ask for more; and it fell to Oliver Twist.

30 The evening arrived; the boys took their places. The master, in his cook's uniform, stationed himself at the copper; his pauper assistants ranged themselves behind him; the gruel was served out; and a long grace was said over the short commons. The gruel disappeared; the boys

whispered to each other, and winked at Oliver, while his next neighbours nudged him. Child as he was, he was desperate with hunger, and reckless with misery. He rose from the table, and advancing to the master, basin and spoon in hand, said: somewhat alarmed at his own temerity:

40   'Please, sir, I want some more.'

The master was a fat, healthy man; but he turned very pale. He gazed in stupefied astonishment on the small rebel for some seconds, and then clung for support to the copper. The assistants were paralysed with wonder; the boys with fear.

'What!' said the master at length, in a faint voice.

'Please, sir,' replied Oliver, 'I want some more.'

The master aimed a blow at Oliver's head with the ladle, pinioned him in his arms, and shrieked aloud for the beadle.

50   The board were sitting in solemn conclave, when Mr Bumble rushed into the room in great excitement, and addressing the gentleman in the high chair, said,

'Mr Limbkins, I beg your pardon, sir! Oliver Twist has asked for more!' There was a general start. Horror was depicted on every countenance.

'For *more*!' said Mr Limbkins. 'Compose yourself, Bumble, and answer me distinctly. Do I understand that he has asked for more, after he had eaten the supper allotted by the dietary?'

60   'He did, sir,' replied Bumble.

'That boy will be hung,' said the gentleman in the white waistcoat; 'I know that boy will be hung.'

Nobody controverted the prophetic gentleman's opinion. An animated discussion took place. Oliver was ordered into instant confinement; and a bill was next morning pasted on the outside of the gate, offering a reward of five pounds to anybody who would take Oliver Twist off the hands of the parish. In other words, five pounds and Oliver Twist were offered to any man or woman

70   who wanted an apprentice to any trade, business, or calling.

Macbeth

WILLIAM SHAKESPEARE (ABRIDGED BY LEON GARFIELD)

The curtain rises on a wild heath under a dark, ragged sky. Thunder and lightning. Three hideous old women, huddled together, screaming with malignant laughter.

1st Witch   When shall we three meet again?
In thunder, lightning, or in rain?

2nd Witch   When the hurly-burly's done,
when the battle's lost and won!

1st Witch   Where the place?

2nd Witch   Upon the heath!

3rd Witch   There to meet with Macbeth!

They stare at one another, and nod.

All   Fair is foul and foul is fair: hover
through the fog and filthy air!

Thunder and lightning. The witches vanish.

The battle is for Scotland itself. Norway has invaded. In the midst of the mad confusion of battle, the gigantic figures of Macbeth and Banquo, his companion-in-arms, lay about them with ceaseless swords. They are the great generals of Duncan, lawful king of Scotland. Presently the battle subsides. The survivors cheer and raise their swords and spears to Macbeth, the victor. He waves his sword in acknowledgement; and Banquo, taking up a drum from a fallen boy, rattles out a roll of triumph.

In the royal camp, good king Duncan learns with joy of Macbeth's victory; but at the same time, hears of the treachery of the Thane of Cawdor, who has been captured. Sadly, he shakes his head.

Duncan	There's no art to find the mind's construction in the face. He was a gentleman on whom I built an absolute trust. Go pronounce his present death, and with his former title greet Macbeth. What he hath lost, noble Macbeth hath won.

The heath. Madman's weather! Macbeth and Banquo are on their way to the royal camp.

Macbeth	So fair and foul a day I have not seen.

Suddenly they halt. Their way is barred by three hideous old women!

Banquo	What are these, withered and so wild in their attire?

They do not answer. Banquo thumps on his drum.

Banquo	Live you? Or are you aught that man may question?

One by one, the witches raise their skinny fingers to their lips. They gaze at Macbeth.

Macbeth	Speak if you can! What are you?
1st Witch	All hail, Macbeth, hail to thee, Thane of Glamis!

Banquo thumps in agreement.

2nd Witch	All hail, Macbeth, hail to thee, Thane of Cawdor!

11

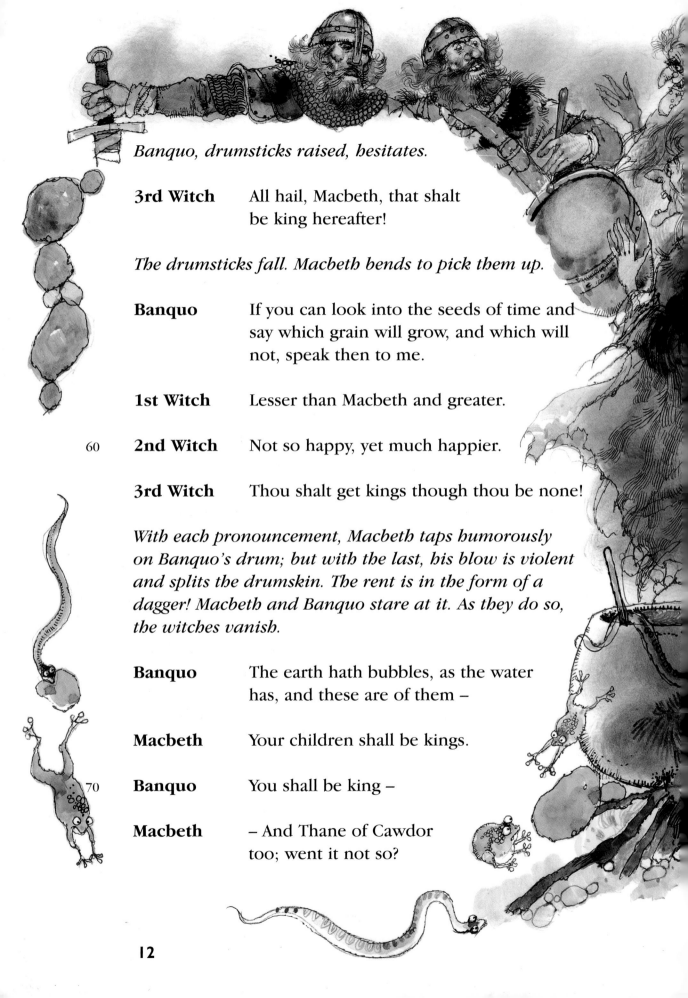

Banquo, drumsticks raised, hesitates.

3rd Witch   All hail, Macbeth, that shalt
be king hereafter!

The drumsticks fall. Macbeth bends to pick them up.

Banquo   If you can look into the seeds of time and
say which grain will grow, and which will
not, speak then to me.

1st Witch   Lesser than Macbeth and greater.

60   **2nd Witch**   Not so happy, yet much happier.

3rd Witch   Thou shalt get kings though thou be none!

*With each pronouncement, Macbeth taps humorously
on Banquo's drum; but with the last, his blow is violent
and splits the drumskin. The rent is in the form of a
dagger! Macbeth and Banquo stare at it. As they do so,
the witches vanish.*

Banquo   The earth hath bubbles, as the water
has, and these are of them –

Macbeth   Your children shall be kings.

70   **Banquo**   You shall be king –

Macbeth   – And Thane of Cawdor
too; went it not so?

As they stare into the terrible air, two ghostly figures appear. As they draw near, they are seen to be two messengers from the king: Rosse and Angus. They salute Macbeth.

Rosse The king hath happily received, Macbeth, the news of thy success. Everyone did bear thy praises, in his kingdom's great defence, and poured them down before him. He bade me, from him, call thee Thane of Cawdor!

Banquo *(aside)* What! Can the Devil speak true?

Macbeth The Thane of Cawdor lives; why do you dress me in borrowed robes?

Angus Who was the Thane lives yet; but under heavy judgement bears that life which he deserves to lose.

Macbeth, in high excitement, turns aside.

Macbeth Glamis, and Thane of Cawdor! Two truths are told, as happy prologues to the swelling act of the imperial theme! Stars, hide your fires! Let not light see my black and deep desires!

Illustrated by Victor G. Ambrus

RIKKI-TIKKI-TAVI
FROM THE JUNGLE BOOK

RUDYARD KIPLING

Rikki is a mongoose who lives with Teddy and his family. Nag, the cobra, is dead, and Nagaina, his wife, wants revenge on the family. With the help of Darzee, the tailor-bird, and his wife, Rikki sets out to hunt down Nagaina.

Darzee was a feather-brained little fellow who could never hold more than one idea at a time in his head; and just because he knew that Nagaina's children were born in eggs like his own, he didn't think at first that it was fair to kill them. But his wife was a sensible bird, and she knew that cobra's eggs meant young cobras later on; so she flew off from the nest, and left Darzee to keep the babies warm, and continue his song about the death of Nag. Darzee was very like a man in some ways.

10   She fluttered in front of Nagaina by the rubbish-heap, and cried out: "Oh, my wing is broken! The boy in the house threw a stone at me and broke it." Then she fluttered more desperately than ever.

Nagaina lifted up her head and hissed: "You warned Rikki-tikki when I would have killed him. Indeed and truly, you've chosen a bad place to be lame in." And she moved toward Darzee's wife, slipping along over the dust.

"The boy broke it with a stone!" shrieked Darzee's wife.

"Well, it may be some consolation to you when you're
20   dead to know that I shall settle accounts with the boy. My husband lies on the rubbish-heap this morning, but before night the boy in the house will lie very still. What is the use of running away? I am sure to catch you. Little fool, look at me!"

Darzee's wife knew better than to do *that*, for a bird who looks at a snake's eyes gets so frightened that she cannot move. Darzee's wife fluttered on, piping sorrowfully, and never leaving the ground, and Nagaina quickened her pace.

Rikki-tikki heard them going up the path from the
30   stables, and he raced for the end of the melon-patch near

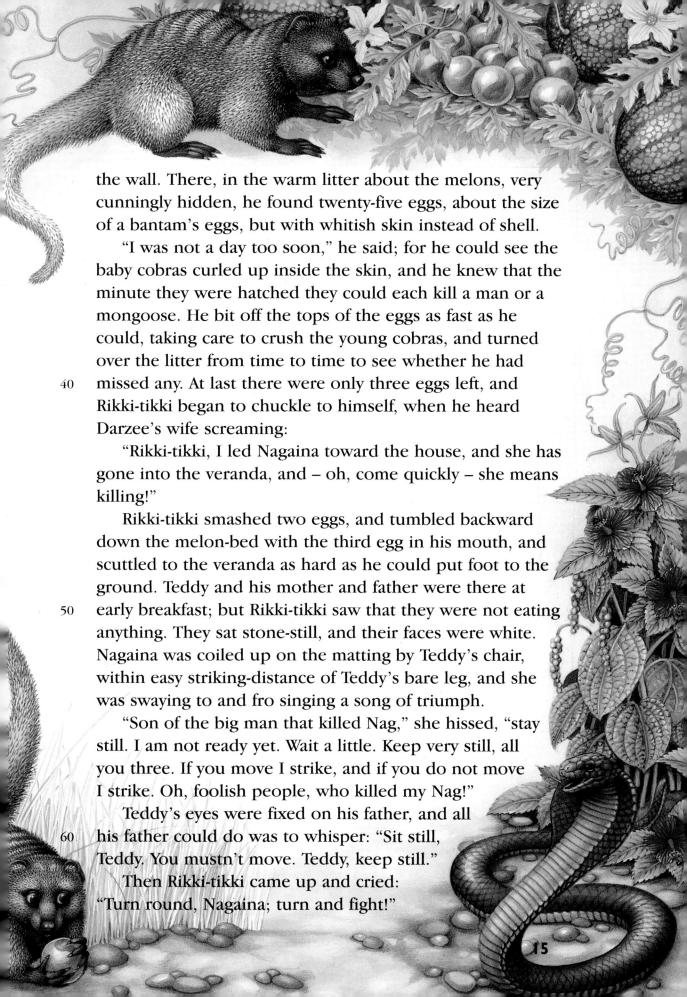

the wall. There, in the warm litter about the melons, very cunningly hidden, he found twenty-five eggs, about the size of a bantam's eggs, but with whitish skin instead of shell.

"I was not a day too soon," he said; for he could see the baby cobras curled up inside the skin, and he knew that the minute they were hatched they could each kill a man or a mongoose. He bit off the tops of the eggs as fast as he could, taking care to crush the young cobras, and turned over the litter from time to time to see whether he had

40   missed any. At last there were only three eggs left, and Rikki-tikki began to chuckle to himself, when he heard Darzee's wife screaming:

"Rikki-tikki, I led Nagaina toward the house, and she has gone into the veranda, and – oh, come quickly – she means killing!"

Rikki-tikki smashed two eggs, and tumbled backward down the melon-bed with the third egg in his mouth, and scuttled to the veranda as hard as he could put foot to the ground. Teddy and his mother and father were there at

50   early breakfast; but Rikki-tikki saw that they were not eating anything. They sat stone-still, and their faces were white. Nagaina was coiled up on the matting by Teddy's chair, within easy striking-distance of Teddy's bare leg, and she was swaying to and fro singing a song of triumph.

"Son of the big man that killed Nag," she hissed, "stay still. I am not ready yet. Wait a little. Keep very still, all you three. If you move I strike, and if you do not move I strike. Oh, foolish people, who killed my Nag!"

Teddy's eyes were fixed on his father, and all

60   his father could do was to whisper: "Sit still, Teddy. You mustn't move. Teddy, keep still."

Then Rikki-tikki came up and cried:
"Turn round, Nagaina; turn and fight!"

"All in good time," said she, without moving her eyes. "I will settle my account with *you* presently. Look at your friends, Rikki-tikki. They are still and white; they are afraid. They dare not move, and if you come a step nearer I strike."

"Look at your eggs," said Rikki-tikki, "in the melon-bed near the wall. Go and look, Nagaina."

The big snake turned half round, and saw the egg on the veranda. "Ah-h! Give it to me," she said.

Rikki-tikki put his paws one on each side of the egg, and his eyes were blood-red. "What price for a snake's egg? For a young cobra? For a young king-cobra? For the last – the very last of the brood? The ants are eating all the others down by the melon-bed."

Nagaina spun clear round, forgetting everything for the sake of the one egg; and Rikki-tikki saw Teddy's father shoot out a big hand, catch Teddy by the shoulder, and drag him across the little table with the teacups, safe and out of reach of Nagaina.

"Tricked! Tricked! Tricked! *Rikk-tck-tck!*" chuckled Rikki-tikki. "The boy is safe, and it was I – I – I that caught Nag by the hood last night in the bathroom." Then he began to jump up and down, all four feet together, his head close to the floor. "He threw me to and fro, but he could not shake me off. He was dead before the big man blew him in two. I did it. *Rikki-tikki-tck-tck!* Come then, Nagaina. Come and fight with me. You shall not be a widow long."

Nagaina saw that she had lost her chance of killing Teddy, and the egg lay between Rikki-tikki's paws. "Give me the egg, Rikki-tikki. Give me the last of my eggs, and I will go away and never come back," she said, lowering her hood.

"Yes, you will go away, and you will never come back; for you will go to the rubbish-heap with Nag. Fight, widow! The big man has gone for his gun! Fight!"

Rikki-tikki was bounding all round Nagaina, keeping just out of reach of her stroke, his little eyes like hot coals. Nagaina gathered herself together, and flung out at him.

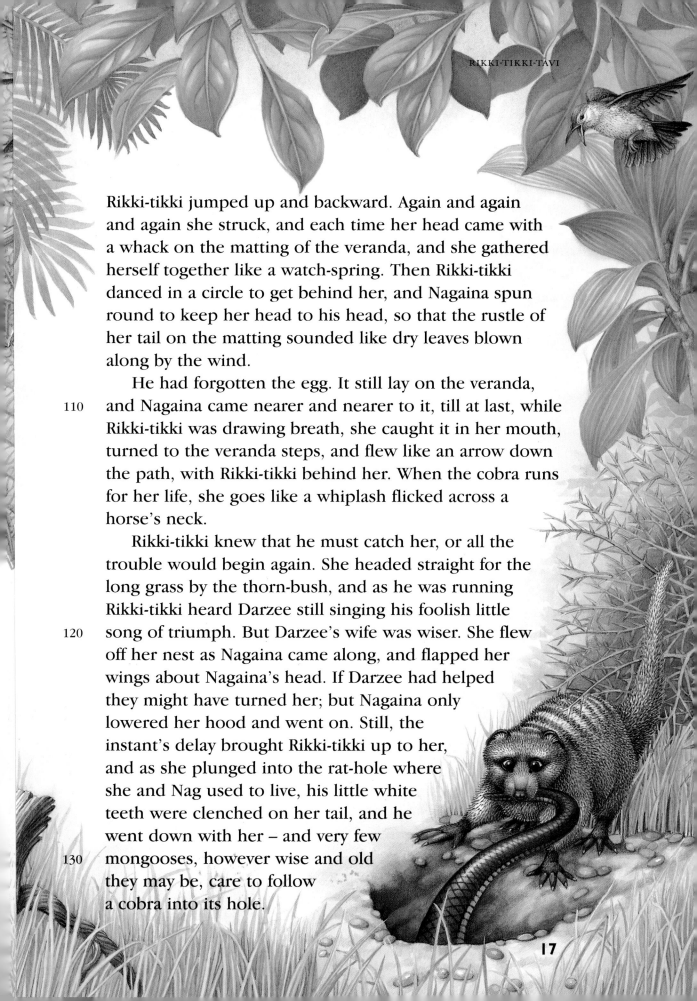

Rikki-tikki jumped up and backward. Again and again and again she struck, and each time her head came with a whack on the matting of the veranda, and she gathered herself together like a watch-spring. Then Rikki-tikki danced in a circle to get behind her, and Nagaina spun round to keep her head to his head, so that the rustle of her tail on the matting sounded like dry leaves blown along by the wind.

110   He had forgotten the egg. It still lay on the veranda, and Nagaina came nearer and nearer to it, till at last, while Rikki-tikki was drawing breath, she caught it in her mouth, turned to the veranda steps, and flew like an arrow down the path, with Rikki-tikki behind her. When the cobra runs for her life, she goes like a whiplash flicked across a horse's neck.

    Rikki-tikki knew that he must catch her, or all the trouble would begin again. She headed straight for the long grass by the thorn-bush, and as he was running Rikki-tikki heard Darzee still singing his foolish little

120   song of triumph. But Darzee's wife was wiser. She flew off her nest as Nagaina came along, and flapped her wings about Nagaina's head. If Darzee had helped they might have turned her; but Nagaina only lowered her hood and went on. Still, the instant's delay brought Rikki-tikki up to her, and as she plunged into the rat-hole where she and Nag used to live, his little white teeth were clenched on her tail, and he went down with her – and very few

130   mongooses, however wise and old they may be, care to follow a cobra into its hole.

HIAWATHA'S CANOE
FROM THE SONG OF HIAWATHA

'Give me of your bark, O Birch-tree!
Of your yellow bark, O Birch-tree!
Growing by the rushing river,
Tall and stately in the valley!
I a light canoe will build me,
Build a swift Cheemaun* for sailing,
That shall float upon the river,
Like a yellow leaf in Autumn,
Like a yellow water-lily.
10   'Lay aside your cloak, O Birch-tree!
Lay aside your white-skin wrapper,
For the Summer-time is coming;
And the sun is warm in heaven,
And you need no white-skin wrapper!'
    Thus aloud cried Hiawatha.

And the tree with all its branches
Rustled in the breeze of morning,
Saying, with a sigh of patience,
    'Take my cloak, O Hiawatha!'
20   With his knife the tree he girdled;
Just beneath its lowest branches,
Just above the roots he cut it,
Till the sap came oozing outward;
Down the trunk from top to bottom,
Sheer he cleft the bark asunder,
With a wooden wedge he raised it,
Stripped it from the trunk unbroken.

* birch/canoe

'Give me of your boughs, O Cedar!
Of your strong and pliant branches,
30   My canoe to make more steady,
Make more strong, and firm beneath me!'
        Through the summit of the Cedar
Went a sound, a cry of horror,
Went a murmur of resistance;
But it whispered, bending downward,
        'Take my boughs, O Hiawatha!'
        Down he hewed the boughs of cedar,
Shaped them straightway to a frame-work,
Like two bows he formed and shaped them,
40   Like two bended bows together.

        'Give me of your roots, O Tamarack!
Of your fibrous roots, O Larch-tree!
My canoe to bind together,
So to bind the ends together
That the water may not enter,
That the river may not wet me!'
        And the Larch, with all its fibres,
Shivered in the air of morning,
Touched his forehead with its tassels,
50   Said, with one long sigh of sorrow,
        'Take them all, O Hiawatha!'
        From the earth he tore the fibres,
Tore the tough roots of the Larch-tree,
Closely sewed the bark together,
Bound it closely to the frame-work.

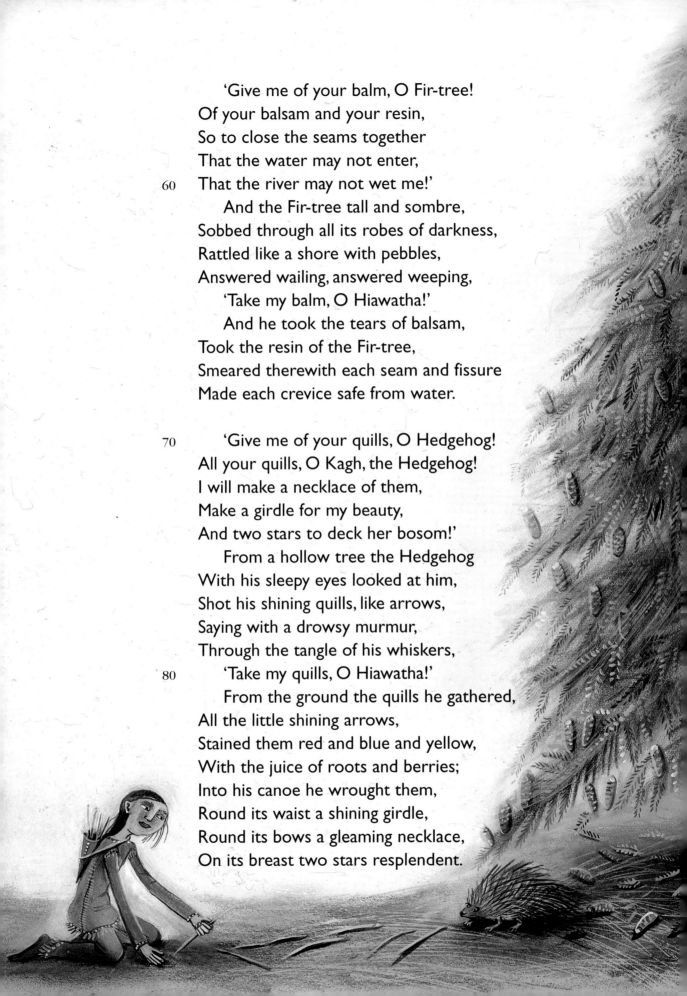

'Give me of your balm, O Fir-tree!
Of your balsam and your resin,
So to close the seams together
That the water may not enter,
60 That the river may not wet me!'
And the Fir-tree tall and sombre,
Sobbed through all its robes of darkness,
Rattled like a shore with pebbles,
Answered wailing, answered weeping,
'Take my balm, O Hiawatha!'
And he took the tears of balsam,
Took the resin of the Fir-tree,
Smeared therewith each seam and fissure
Made each crevice safe from water.

70 'Give me of your quills, O Hedgehog!
All your quills, O Kagh, the Hedgehog!
I will make a necklace of them,
Make a girdle for my beauty,
And two stars to deck her bosom!'
From a hollow tree the Hedgehog
With his sleepy eyes looked at him,
Shot his shining quills, like arrows,
Saying with a drowsy murmur,
Through the tangle of his whiskers,
80 'Take my quills, O Hiawatha!'
From the ground the quills he gathered,
All the little shining arrows,
Stained them red and blue and yellow,
With the juice of roots and berries;
Into his canoe he wrought them,
Round its waist a shining girdle,
Round its bows a gleaming necklace,
On its breast two stars resplendent.

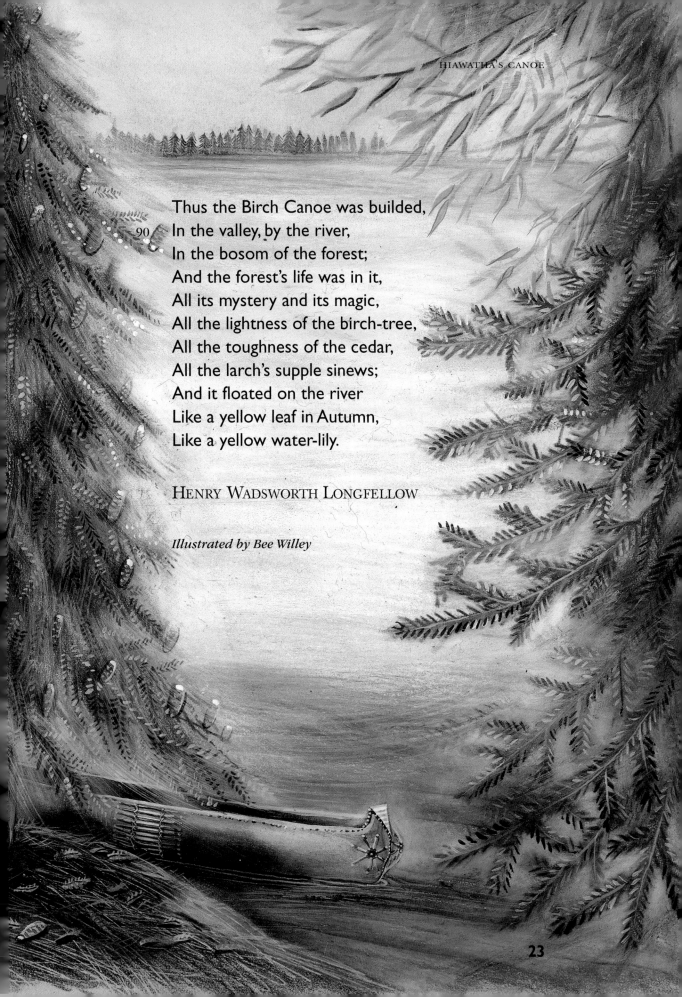

Thus the Birch Canoe was builded,
90 In the valley, by the river,
In the bosom of the forest;
And the forest's life was in it,
All its mystery and its magic,
All the lightness of the birch-tree,
All the toughness of the cedar,
All the larch's supple sinews;
And it floated on the river
Like a yellow leaf in Autumn,
Like a yellow water-lily.

HENRY WADSWORTH LONGFELLOW

Illustrated by Bee Willey

The Secret Garden

FRANCES HODGSON BURNETT

There was something mysterious in the air that morning. Nothing was done in its regular order and several of the native servants seemed missing, while those whom Mary saw slunk or hurried about with ashy and scared faces. But no one would tell her anything, and her Ayah did not come. She was actually left alone as the morning went on, and at last wandered out into the garden and began to play by herself under a tree near the veranda. She pretended that she was making a flower-bed, and she stuck big scarlet

10 hibiscus blossoms into little heaps of earth, all the time growing more and more angry and muttering to herself the things she would say and the names she would call Saidie when she returned. 'Pig! Pig! Daughter of Pigs!' she said, because to call a native a pig is the worst insult of all.

She was grinding her teeth and saying this over and over again when she heard her mother come out on the veranda with someone. She was with a fair young man, and they stood talking together in low strange voices. Mary knew the fair young man who looked like a boy. She had heard that

20 he was a very young officer who had just come from England. The child stared at him, but she stared most at her mother. She always did this when she had a chance to see her, because the Memsahib – Mary used to call her that oftener than anything else – was such a tall, slim, pretty person and wore such lovely clothes. Her hair was like curly silk and she had a delicate little nose which seemed to be disdaining things, and she had large laughing eyes. All her clothes were thin and floating, and Mary said they were 'full of lace'. They looked fuller of lace than ever this morning,

30 but her eyes were not laughing at all. They were large and scared and lifted imploringly to the fair boy officer's face.

'Is it so very bad? Oh, is it?' Mary heard her say.

'Awfully,' the young man answered in a trembling voice.

'Awfully, Mrs Lennox. You ought to have gone to the hills two weeks ago.'

The Memsahib wrung her hands.

'Oh, I know I ought!' she cried. 'I only stayed to go to that silly dinner-party. What a fool I was!'

At that very moment such a loud sound of wailing broke out from the servants' quarters that she clutched the young man's arm, and Mary stood shivering from head to foot. The wailing grew wilder and wilder.

'What is it? What is it?' Mrs Lennox gasped.

'Someone has died,' answered the boy officer. 'You did not say it had broken out among your servants.'

'I did not know!' the Memsahib cried. 'Come with me! Come with me!' and she turned and ran into the house.

After that, appalling things happened, and the mysteriousness of the morning was explained to Mary. The cholera had broken out in its most fatal form and people were dying like flies. The Ayah had been taken ill in the night, and it was because she had just died that the servants had wailed in the huts. Before the next day three other servants were dead and others had run away in terror. There was panic on every side, and dying people in all the bungalows.

During the confusion and bewilderment of the second day Mary hid herself in the nursery and was forgotten by everyone. Nobody thought of her, nobody wanted her, and strange things happened of which she knew nothing. Mary alternately cried and slept through the hours. She only knew that people were ill and that she heard mysterious and frightening sounds. Once she crept into the dining-room and found it empty, though a partly finished meal was on the table and chairs and plates looked as if they had been hastily pushed back when the diners rose suddenly for some reason. The child ate some fruit and biscuits, and being thirsty she drank a glass of wine which stood nearly filled. It was sweet, and she did not know how strong it was. Very soon it made her intensely drowsy, and she went back to her nursery and shut herself in again, frightened by cries she heard in the huts and by the hurrying sound of feet. The wine made her so sleepy that she could scarcely keep her eyes open, and she lay down on her bed and knew nothing more for a long time.

Many things happened during the hours in which she slept so heavily, but she was not disturbed by the wails and the sound of things being carried in and out of the bungalow.

When she awakened she lay and stared at the wall. The house was perfectly still. She had never known it to be so silent before. She heard neither voices nor footsteps, and wondered if everybody had got well of the cholera and all the trouble was over. She wondered also who would take care of her now her Ayah was dead. There would be a new Ayah, and perhaps she would know some new stories. Mary had been rather tired of the old ones. She did not cry because her nurse had died. She was not an affectionate child and had never cared much for anyone. The noise and hurrying about and wailing over the cholera had frightened her, and she had been angry because no one seemed to remember that she was alive. Everyone was too panic-stricken to think of a little girl no one was fond of. When people had the cholera it seemed that they remembered nothing but themselves. But if everyone had got well again, surely someone would remember and come to look for her.

But no one came, and as she lay waiting the house seemed to grow more and more silent. She heard something rustling on the matting, and when she looked down she saw a little snake gliding along and watching her with eyes like jewels. She was not frightened, because he was a harmless little thing who would not hurt her, and he seemed in a hurry to get out of the room. He slipped under the door as she watched him.

'How queer and quiet it is,' she said. 'It sounds as if there was no one in the bungalow but me and the snake.'

Almost the next minute she heard footsteps in the compound, and then on the veranda. They were men's footsteps, and the men entered the bungalow and talked in low voices. No one went to meet or speak to them, and they seemed to open doors and look into rooms.

110 'What desolation!' she heard one voice say. 'That pretty, pretty woman! I suppose the child, too. I heard there was a child, though no one ever saw her.'

Mary was standing in the middle of the nursery when they opened the door a few minutes later. She looked an ugly, cross little thing and was frowning because she was beginning to be hungry and feel disgracefully neglected. The first man who came in was a large officer she had once seen talking to her father. He looked tired and troubled, but when he saw her he was so startled that he almost jumped back.

120 'Barney!' he cried out. 'There is a child here! A child alone! In a place like this! Mercy on us, who is she?'

'I am Mary Lennox,' the little girl said, drawing herself up stiffly. She thought the man was very rude to call her father's bungalow 'A place like this!' 'I fell asleep when everyone had the cholera and I have only just wakened up. Why does nobody come?'

'It is the child no one ever saw!' exclaimed the man, turning to his companions. 'She has actually been forgotten!'

130 'Why was I forgotten?' Mary said, stamping her foot. 'Why does nobody come?'

The young man whose name was Barney looked at her very sadly. Mary even thought she saw him wink his eyes as if to wink tears away.

'Poor little kid!' he said. 'There is nobody left to come.'

It was in that strange and sudden way that Mary found out that she had neither father nor mother left; that they had died and been carried away in the night, and that the few native servants who had not died also had left the house

140 as quickly as they could get out of it, none of them even remembering that there was a Missie Sahib. That was why the place was so quiet. It was true that there was no one in the bungalow but herself and the little rustling snake.

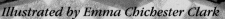

Illustrated by Emma Chichester Clark

There Was an Old Man of Dumbree

There was an Old Man of Dumbree,
Who taught little Owls to drink Tea;
    For he said, 'To eat mice
    Is not proper or nice,'
That amiable Man of Dumbree.

EDWARD LEAR

There Was an Old Person of Burton

There was an Old Person of Burton,
Whose answers were rather uncertain;
    When they said, 'How d'ye do?'
    He replied, 'Who are you?'
That distressing Old Person of Burton.

EDWARD LEAR

A Tutor Who Tooted the Flute

A tutor who tooted the flute
Tried to tutor two tooters to toot.
   Said the two to the tutor,
   'Is it harder to toot or
To tutor two tooters to toot?'

CAROLYN WELLS

There Was an Old Man in a Trunk

There was an old man in a trunk,
Who inquired of his wife, 'Am I drunk?'
   She replied with regret,
   'I'm afraid so, my pet.'
And he answered, 'It's just as I thunk.'

OGDEN NASH

Illustrated by Uwe Mayer

Black Dot

a black dot
a jelly tot

a scum-nail
a jiggle-tail

a cool kicker
a sitting slicker

a panting puffer
a fly-snuffer

a high hopper
a belly-flopper

a catalogue
    to make me

        frog

LIBBY HOUSTON

The Warning

Just now,
Out of the strange
Still dusk … as strange, as still …
A white moth flew. Why am I grown
So cold?

ADELAIDE CRAPSEY

30

Illustrated by Chloë Cheese

Swap? Sell? Small Ads Sell Fast

1960 Dad. Good runner; needs one or
Two repairs; a few grey hairs but
Nothing a respray couldn't fix.
Would like a 1976 five speed turbo
In exchange: something in the sporty
Twin-carb range.

1930s Granny. Not many like this.
In such clean and rust free state.
You must stop by to view! All chrome
As new, original fascia retained
Upholstery unstained. Passed MOT
Last week: will only swap for some-
Thing quite unique.

1999 low mileage Brother. As eco-
Nomical as any other. Must mention
Does need some attention. Stream-
Lined, rear spoiler. Runs on milk
Baby oil and gripe water. Serviced;
Needs rear wash/wipe. Only one
Owner; not yet run in. Will swap
For anything.

TREVOR MILLUM

Illustrated by Chloë Cheese

Christmas Thank Yous

Dear Auntie
Oh, what a nice jumper
I've always adored powder blue
and fancy you thinking of
orange and pink
for the stripes
how clever of you

Dear Uncle
The soap is
terrific
So
useful
and such a kind thought and
how did you guess that
I'd just used the last of
the soap that last Christmas brought

Dear Gran
Many thanks for the hankies
Now I really can't wait for the flu
and the daisies embroidered
in red round the 'M'
for Michael
how
thoughtful of you

Dear Cousin
What socks!
and the same sort you wear
so you must be
the last word in style
and I'm certain you're right that the
luminous green
will make me stand out a mile

Dear Sister
I quite understand your concern
it's a risk sending jam in the post
But I think I've pulled out
all the big bits
of glass
so it won't taste too sharp
spread on toast

Dear Grandad
Don't fret
I'm delighted
So *don't* think your gift will
offend
I'm not at all hurt
that you gave up this year
and just sent me
a fiver
to spend

MICK GOWAR

Illustrated by Nick Sharratt

Tom's Midnight Garden

PHILIPPA PEARCE

Tom is staying with his uncle and aunt who live in a strange old house. One night, Tom decides to explore.

Tom opened the door wide and let in the moonlight. It flooded in, as bright as daylight – the white daylight that comes before the full rising of the sun. The illumination was perfect, but Tom did not at once turn to see what it showed him of the clock-face. Instead he took a step forward on to the doorstep. He was staring, at first in surprise, then with indignation, at what he saw outside. That they should have deceived him – lied to him – like this! They had said, 'It's not worth your while going out at the back, Tom.' So carelessly they had described it: 'A sort of back-yard, very poky, with rubbish bins. Really, there's nothing to see.'

Nothing... Only this: a great lawn where flower-beds bloomed; a towering fir-tree, and thick, beetle-browed yews that humped their shapes down two sides of the lawn; on the third side, to the right, a greenhouse almost the size of a real house; from each corner of the lawn, a path that twisted away to some other depths of garden, with other trees.

Tom had stepped forward instinctively, catching his breath in surprise; now he let his breath out in a deep sigh. He would steal out here tomorrow, by daylight. They had tried to keep this from him, but they could not stop him now – not his aunt, nor his uncle, nor the back flat tenants, nor even particular Mrs Bartholomew. He would run full tilt over the grass, leaping the flower-beds; he would peer through the glittering panes of the greenhouse – perhaps open the door and go in; he would visit each alcove

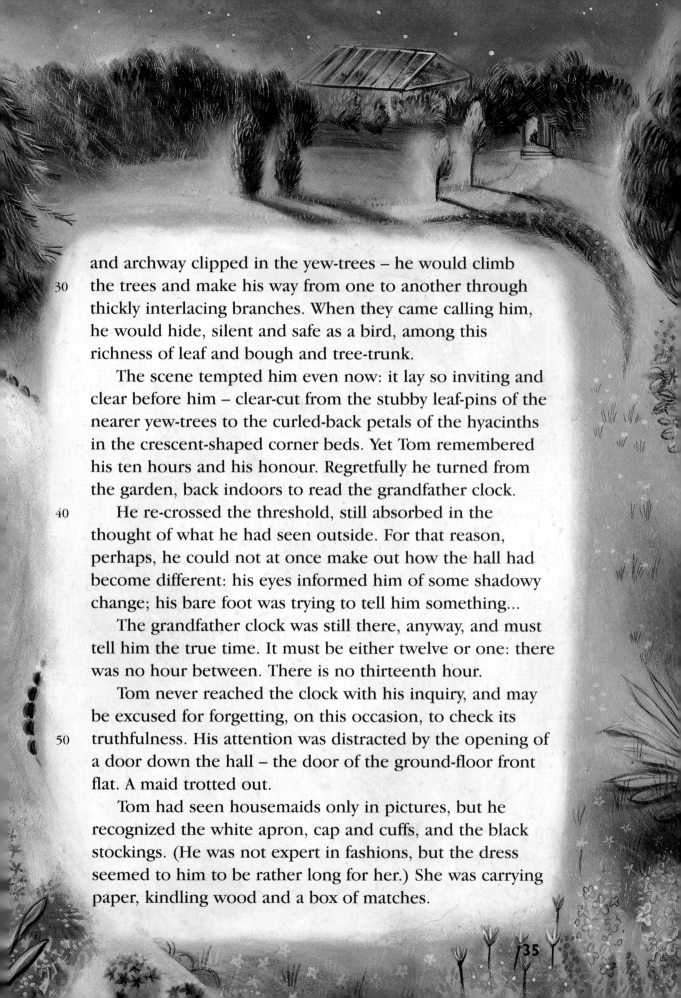

and archway clipped in the yew-trees – he would climb
the trees and make his way from one to another through
thickly interlacing branches. When they came calling him,
he would hide, silent and safe as a bird, among this
richness of leaf and bough and tree-trunk.

The scene tempted him even now: it lay so inviting and
clear before him – clear-cut from the stubby leaf-pins of the
nearer yew-trees to the curled-back petals of the hyacinths
in the crescent-shaped corner beds. Yet Tom remembered
his ten hours and his honour. Regretfully he turned from
the garden, back indoors to read the grandfather clock.

He re-crossed the threshold, still absorbed in the
thought of what he had seen outside. For that reason,
perhaps, he could not at once make out how the hall had
become different: his eyes informed him of some shadowy
change; his bare foot was trying to tell him something…

The grandfather clock was still there, anyway, and must
tell him the true time. It must be either twelve or one: there
was no hour between. There is no thirteenth hour.

Tom never reached the clock with his inquiry, and may
be excused for forgetting, on this occasion, to check its
truthfulness. His attention was distracted by the opening of
a door down the hall – the door of the ground-floor front
flat. A maid trotted out.

Tom had seen housemaids only in pictures, but he
recognized the white apron, cap and cuffs, and the black
stockings. (He was not expert in fashions, but the dress
seemed to him to be rather long for her.) She was carrying
paper, kindling wood and a box of matches.

He had only a second in which to observe these things.
Then he realized that he ought to take cover at once; and
there was no cover to take. Since he must be seen, Tom was
determined to be the first to speak – to explain himself.

He did not feel afraid of the maid: as she came nearer,
he saw that she was only a girl. To warn her of his presence
without startling her, Tom gave a cough; but she did not
seem to hear it. She came on. Tom moved forward into her
line of vision; she looked at him, but looked through him,
too, as though he were not there. Tom's heart jumped in a
way he did not understand. She was passing him.

'I say!' he protested loudly; but she paid not the
slightest attention. She passed him, reached the front door
of the ground-floor back flat, turned the door-handle and
went in. There was no bell-ringing or unlocking of the door.

Tom was left gaping; and, meanwhile, his senses began
to insist upon telling him of experiences even stranger than
this encounter. His one bare foot was on cold flagstone, he
knew; yet there was a contradictory softness and warmth to
this flagstone. He looked down and saw that he was
standing on a rug – a tiger-skin rug. There were other rugs
down the hall. His eyes now took in the whole of the hall –
a hall that was different. No laundry box, no milk bottles,
no travel posters on the walls. The walls were decorated
with a rich variety of other objects instead: a tall Gothic

barometer, a fan of peacock feathers, a huge engraving of a battle (hussars and horses and shot-riddled banners) and many other pictures. There was a big dinner gong, with its wash-leathered gong-stick hanging beside it. There was a large umbrella stand holding umbrellas and walking-sticks and a parasol and an air-gun and what looked like the parts of a fishing-rod. Along the wall projected a series of bracket-
90   shelves, each table-high. They were of oak, except for one towards the middle of the hall, by the grandfather clock. That was of white marble, and it was piled high with glass cases of stuffed birds and animals. Enacted on its chilly surface were scenes of hot bloodshed: an owl clutched a mouse in its claws; a ferret looked up from the killing of its rabbit; in a case in the middle a red fox slunk along with a gamefowl hanging from its jaws.

In all that crowded hall, the only object that Tom recognized was the grandfather clock. He moved towards
100   it, not to read its face, but simply to touch it – to reassure himself that this at least was as he knew it.

His hand was nearly upon it, when he heard a little breath behind him that was the maid passing back the way she had come. For some reason, she did not seem to make as much sound as before. He heard her call only faintly: 'I've lit the fire in the parlour.'

She was making for the door through which she had first come, and, as Tom followed her with his eyes, he received a curious impression: she reached the door, her hand was
110   upon the knob, and then she seemed to go. That was it exactly: she went, but not through the door. She simply thinned out, and went.

Even as he stared at where she had been, Tom became aware of something going on furtively and silently about him. He looked round sharply, and caught the hall in the act of emptying itself of furniture and rugs and pictures. They were not positively going, perhaps, but rather beginning to fail to be there. The Gothic barometer, for instance, was there, before he turned to look at the red fox; when he turned back, the barometer was still there, but it had the appearance of something only sketched against the wall, and the wall was visible through it; meanwhile the fox had slunk into nothingness, and all the other creatures were going with him; and, turning back again swiftly to the barometer, Tom found that gone already.

In a matter of seconds the whole hall was as he had seen it on his first arrival. He stood dumbfounded. He was roused from his stupefaction by the chill of a draught at his back: it reminded him that the garden door was left open. Whatever else had happened, he had really opened that door; and he must shut it. He must go back to bed.

He closed the door after a long look: 'I shall come back,' he promised silently to the trees and the lawn and the greenhouse.

Upstairs, again, in bed, he pondered more calmly on what he had seen in the hall. Had it been a dream? Another possible explanation occurred to him: ghosts. That was what they could all have been: ghosts. The hall was haunted by the ghost of a housemaid and a barometer and a stuffed

140 fox and a stuffed owl and by the ghosts of dozens of other things. Indeed, if it were haunted at all, the hall was overhaunted.

Ghosts… Tom doubtfully put his hand up out of the bedclothes to see if his hair were standing on end. It was not. Nor, he remembered, had he felt any icy chill when the maid had looked at him and through him.

He was dissatisfied with his own explanation, and suddenly sick of needing to explain at all. It was not as if the hall were of great interest, with or without a maid and

150 all the rest; the garden was the thing. That was real. Tomorrow he would go into it: he almost had the feel of tree-trunks between his hands as he climbed; he could almost smell the heavy blooming of the hyacinths in the corner beds. He remembered that smell from home: indoors, from his mother's bulb pots, at Christmas and the New Year; outside, in their flower-bed, in the late spring. He fell asleep thinking of home.

Illustrated by Bee Willey

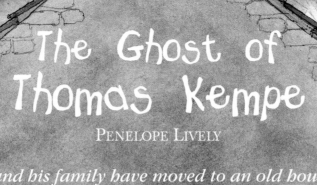

The Ghost of Thomas Kempe

PENELOPE LIVELY

James and his family have moved to an old house, not realizing that a ghost lives there too. The ghost seems especially keen to annoy James.

After lunch the pewter clouds that had been slowly massing above the village all morning opened up into determined, continuous rain. Mrs Harrison said she felt as though she was being drowned from without as well as within, and went to bed with a book. Mr Harrison went to sleep in an armchair. Helen went to see a friend.

James remembered he had some homework to do. He climbed up to his bedroom, closed the door, and sat down at his table. Tim padded round the room once or twice, 10 jumped up on the bed, swirled the covers around several times until he achieved a satisfactory position, and went to sleep. Outside, the rain drummed on the roof and poured in oily rivers down the window.

James opened his project book, looked at his notes, and began to write. It was a project about ancient Greece, and he was enjoying it. He looked things up, and wrote, and stuck some pictures in, and thought about Alexander the Great, and drew a picture of a vase with blokes having a battle on it, and forgot about everything except what he was
20 doing. Around him, the room rustled occasionally: a piece of paper floated to the floor, and a pen rolled across the table. Tim twitched in his sleep.

All of a sudden something nudged James's foot. It was a sheet from his exercise book. He picked it up and read:

I am glad to see thee at thy studies, though I lyke not thy bookes. Where is thy Latin? & where are thy volumes of Astrolgie? But to our businesse... I have putt out the water for people to knowe wee are seeking thieves: it will doe for a crystalle. Thy father's baldnesse could be stayed by bathing with an ointment made from the leaves of Yarrow (a herb of Venus) but there is no cure for thy mother's ailmente of
30 the eyes for it is caused by wytcherie. Nothing will suffice save to seeke out the wytch & bring her to justice. This muste wee doe with all haste.

James swung round in his chair. Then he got up and searched the room, even looking under the bed. There was nothing to be seen, and nothing moved.

He read the note again. The reference to his father's baldness he found particularly annoying. That was cheek, that was. In fact, he thought, he's a proper busybody, that's what he is.

40 And then he remembered Simon's suggestion. All right then, let's have a go. Let's try talking to him.

He cleared his throat, feeling distinctly foolish at addressing the empty room, even though there was no one to hear, and said, 'Er – Mr Kempe.'

Silence. Tim uncurled himself and looked up, yawning.

James took a deep breath and said firmly,
50 'I'm afraid I can't do the things you want me to do because people don't go in much for sorcery nowadays. I don't think they'd really be very interested. You see we don't use those kind of medicines now because we've got penicillin and that and we've got policemen for finding out if anyone's pinched things and catching thieves and my mother gets hay-fever every year and it really isn't anything to do with witchcraft it's because she's allergic to...'

60 There was a loud crash behind him. He whirled round. One of his clay pots had fallen on to the floor and smashed. Even as he looked, a second one raised itself from the shelf, flew across the room, narrowly missing his right ear, and dashed itself against the opposite wall. Tim leapt from the bed and rushed about the room, barking furiously.

'Hey! Stop that!' shouted James.

A gust of wind swept wildly round the room, lifting all the papers on the table and whirling them about the floor. The ink-bottle scuttered to the edge of the table and hung there till James grabbed hold of it with one hand while with the other he made ineffectual dabs at the flying pages from his project book.

'Here! Lay off! Cut it out!'

The door opened and banged itself shut again, twice. The windows rattled as though assaulted by a sudden thunderstorm. The calendar above the bed reared up, twitched itself from the hook, and flapped to the floor. A glass of water on the bedside table tipped over and broke, making a large puddle on the mat. Downstairs, James could hear the sitting-room door open, and his father's footsteps across the hall.

'Please!' he squeaked breathlessly, using one hand to steady the chair, which was bucking about like a ship in a storm, while with the other he warded off Volume 1 of *A Child's Encyclopaedia* which had risen from the bookshelf and hurled itself at his head.

'Please! Don't! Look, perhaps I could...'

Mrs Harrison's bedroom door opened and her voice could be heard saying something loud and not very friendly on the landing. Mr Harrison was coming up the stairs.

The bedcover whisked off the bed, whirled round once or twice, and sank to the floor, engulfing a frantic Tim in its folds.

'All right!' shouted James. 'All right! I'll do it. Anything. If you stop.'

The room subsided. Tim struggled out from under the bedcover and dived for the shelter of the bed. The door opened and Mr Harrison came in. James stood amid the wreckage of his room and waited for the storm to break.

Illustrated by Victor G. Ambrus

43

The Listeners

'Is there anybody there?' said the Traveller,
　　Knocking on the moonlit door;
And his horse in the silence champed the grasses
　　Of the forest's ferny floor:
And a bird flew up out of the turret,
　　Above the Traveller's head:
And he smote upon the door again a second time;
　　'Is there anybody there?' he said.
But no one descended to the Traveller;
　　No head from the leaf-fringed sill
Leaned over and looked into his grey eyes,
　　Where he stood perplexed and still.
But only a host of phantom listeners
　　That dwelt in the lone house then
Stood listening in the quiet of the moonlight
　　To that voice from the world of men:
Stood thronging the faint moonbeams on the dark stair,
　　That goes down to the empty hall,
Hearkening in an air stirred and shaken
　　By the lonely Traveller's call.
And he felt in his heart their strangeness,
　　Their stillness answering his cry,
While his horse moved, cropping the dark turf,
　　'Neath the starred and leafy sky;
For he suddenly smote on the door, even
　　Louder, and lifted his head:—
'Tell them I came and no one answered,
　　That I kept my word,' he said.
Never the least stir made the listeners,
　　Though every word he spake
Fell echoing through the shadowiness of the still house
　　From the one man left awake:
Ay, they heard his foot upon the stirrup,
　　And the sound of iron on stone,
And how the silence surged softly backward,
　　When the plunging hoofs were gone.

WALTER DE LA MARE

44

Illustrated by Emma Chichester Clark

Silver

Slowly, silently, now the moon
Walks the night in her silver shoon;
This way, and that, she peers, and sees
Silver fruit upon silver trees;
One by one the casements catch
Her beams beneath the silvery thatch;
Couched in his kennel, like a log,
With paws of silver sleeps the dog;
From their shadowy cote the white breasts peep
Of doves in a silver-feathered sleep;
A harvest mouse goes scampering by,
With silver claws and silver eye;
And moveless fish in the water gleam,
By silver reeds in a silver stream.

WALTER DE LA MARE

45

Illustrated by Emma Chichester Clark

The Silver Sword

Ian Serraillier

Nazi storm troopers have taken Joseph Balicki away from his family in Poland. One night, when the three children are asleep, they come back for his wife.

What had happened to Joseph's family that night over a year ago when the Nazi storm troopers called at the schoolhouse? Was what Mrs Krause said true? Had they taken his wife away? Had they returned and blown up the house with the children in it?

This is what happened.

That night there was an inch of snow on the roofs of Warsaw. Ruth and Bronia were asleep in the bedroom next to their mother's. Edek's room was on the top floor, below
10 the attic. He was asleep when the Nazi soldiers broke into the house, but he woke up when he heard a noise outside his door. He jumped out of bed and turned the handle. The door was locked. He shouted and banged on it with his fists, but it was no use. Then he lay down with his ear to the floor and listened. In his mother's room the men were rapping out orders, but he could not catch a word that was said.

In the ceiling was a small trapdoor that led into the attic. A ladder lay between his bed and the wall. Quietly he
20 removed it, hooked it under the trap, and climbed up.

Hidden between the water tank and the felt jacket round it was his rifle. He was a member of the Boys' Rifle Brigade and had used it in the siege of Warsaw. It was loaded. He took it out and quickly climbed down to his room.

The noise in the room below had stopped. Looking out of the window into the street, he saw a Nazi van waiting outside the front door. Two storm troopers were taking his mother down the steps, and she was struggling.
30 Quietly Edek lifted the window sash till it was half open.

He dared not shoot in case he hit his mother. He had to
wait till she was in the van and the doors were being closed.

His first shot hit a soldier in the arm. Yelling, he jumped
in beside the driver. With the next two shots Edek aimed at
the tyres. One punctured the rear wheel, but the van got
away, skidding and roaring up the street. His other shots
went wide.

With the butt of his rifle he broke down the door and
ran down to his sisters. They were locked in, too. He burst
40   open the door.

Bronia was sitting up in bed and Ruth was trying to calm
her. She was almost as distraught herself. Only the effort to
comfort Bronia kept her from losing control.

'I hit one of the swine,' said Edek.

'That was very silly of you,' said Ruth. 'They'll come back
for us now.'

'I couldn't let them take Mother away like that,' said
Edek. 'Oh, be quiet, Bronia! Howling won't help.'

'We must get away from here before they come back,'
50   said Ruth.

With some difficulty she dressed Bronia, while Edek went into the hall to fetch overcoats and boots and fur caps.

There was no time for Ruth to dress properly. She put on a coat over her nightdress and wound a woollen scarf round Bronia.

'We can't get out the front way,' said Edek. 'There's another van coming. I heard the whistle.'

'What about the back?' said Ruth.

'The wall's too high. We'd never get Bronia over. Besides, there are Nazis billeted in that street. There's only one way – over the roof.'

'We'll never manage that,' said Ruth.

'It's the only way,' said Edek. 'I'll carry Bronia. Be quick – I can hear them coming.'

He picked up the sobbing Bronia and led the way upstairs. He was wearing his father's thick overcoat over his pyjamas, a pair of stout boots on his bare feet, and his rifle slung on his back.

When they were all up in the attic, he smashed the sky-light.

'Now listen, Bronia,' said Edek. 'If you make a sound, we shall never see Mother again. We shall all be killed.'

'Of course we shall see her again,' Ruth added. 'But only if you do as Edek says.'

He climbed through the skylight on to the slippery roof. Ruth handed Bronia up to him, then followed herself. The bitterly cold air made her gasp.

'I can't carry you yet, Bronia,' said Edek. 'You must walk behind me and hold on to the rifle. It doesn't matter if you slip, if you hold on to the rifle. And don't look down.'

The first few steps – as far as the V between the chimney and the roof ridge – were ghastly. Edek made a dash for it, grabbed the telephone bracket and hauled himself up, with Bronia clinging on behind. She was speechless with terror. He reached back and hauled Ruth up after him.

After a few moments' rest, they slid down a few feet on to a flat part that jutted out, a sort of parapet.

48

The roof ridge lay between them and the street, so they could not see what was happening down there. But they could hear shouting, the whine of cars, the screech of brakes.

90

Luckily for them, all the houses on this side of the school were joined together in one long terrace, otherwise they could not have got away. Even so, it was a miracle that none of their slips and tumbles ended in disaster.

They must have gone fully a hundred yards when the first explosion shook the air. A sheet of fire leapt up from their home into the frosty night sky. They fell flat in the snow and lay there. The roof shook, the whole city seemed to tremble. Another explosion. Smoke and flames poured from the windows. Sparks showered into the darkness.

100

'Come along,' said Edek. 'We shan't let them have us now.'

With growing confidence they hurried along the roof-tops. At last, by descending a twisted fire escape, they reached street level. On and on they hurried, not knowing or caring where they went so long as they left those roaring flames behind them.

They did not stop till the fire was far away and the pale winter dawn was breaking.

110

They took shelter in the cellar of a bombed house. Exhausted, huddled together for warmth, they slept till long after midday, when cold and hunger woke them.

Illustrated by Brad Gray

The War of the Worlds

H G WELLS

A colossal extraterrestrial cylinder has landed on the Common, making a huge crater. A crowd has gathered to see what will happen next.

I saw a young man, a shop assistant in Woking I believe he was, standing on the cylinder and trying to scramble out of the hole again. The crowd had pushed him in.

The end of the cylinder was being screwed out from within. Nearly two feet of shining screw projected. Somebody blundered against me, and I narrowly missed being pitched on to the top of the screw. I turned, and as I did so the screw must have come out, and the lid of the cylinder fell upon the gravel with a ringing concussion. I

10   stuck my elbow into the person behind me and turned my head towards the Thing again. For a moment that circular cavity seemed perfectly black. I had the sunset in my eyes.

I think everyone expected to see a man emerge – possibly something a little unlike us terrestrial men, but in all essentials a man. I know I did. But, looking, I presently saw something stirring within the shadow – greyish billowy movements, one above another, and then two luminous discs like eyes. Then something resembling a little grey snake, about the thickness of a walking-stick, coiled up out

20   of the writhing middle, and wriggled in the air towards me – and then another.

A sudden chill came over me. There was a loud shriek from a woman behind. I half turned, keeping my eyes fixed upon the cylinder still, from which other tentacles were now projecting, and began pushing my way back from the edge of the pit. I saw astonishment giving place to horror on the faces of the people about me. I heard inarticulate exclamations on all sides. There was a general movement backward. I saw the shopman struggling still on the edge

30   of the pit. I found myself alone, and saw the people on the other side of the pit running off, Stent among them.

I looked again at the cylinder, and ungovernable terror gripped me. I stood petrified and staring.

A big greyish, rounded bulk, the size perhaps, of a bear, was rising slowly and painfully out of the cylinder. As it bulged up and caught the light, it glistened like wet leather. Two large dark-coloured eyes were regarding me steadfastly. It was rounded, and had, one might say, a face. There was a mouth under the eyes, the lipless brim of which quivered
40   and panted, and dropped saliva. The body heaved and pulsated convulsively. A lank tentacular appendage gripped the edge of the cylinder, another swayed in the air.

Those who have never seen a living Martian can scarcely imagine the strange horror of their appearance. The peculiar V-shaped mouth with its pointed upper lip, the absence of brow ridges, the absence of a chin beneath the wedge-like lower lip, the incessant quivering of this mouth, the Gorgon groups of tentacles, the tumultuous breathing of the lungs in a strange atmosphere, the evident heaviness
50   and painfulness of movement, due to the greater gravitational energy of the earth – above all, the extraordinary intensity of the immense eyes – culminated in an effect akin to nausea. There was something fungoid in the oily brown skin, something in the clumsy deliberation of their tedious movements unspeakably terrible. Even at this first encounter, this first glimpse, I was overcome with disgust and dread.

Suddenly the monster vanished. It had toppled over the brim of the cylinder and fallen into the pit, with a thud like
60   the fall of a great mass of leather. I heard it give a peculiar thick cry, and forthwith another of these creatures appeared in the deep shadow of the aperture.

At that my rigour of terror passed away. I turned and, running madly, made for the first group of trees, perhaps a hundred yards away; but I ran slantingly and stumbling, for I could not avert my face from these things.

Illustrated by Stephen Player

The Lottie Project

Jacqueline Wilson

Miss Beckworth. She was new so I thought she'd be young. When you get a new young teacher they're often ever so strict the first few weeks just to show you who's boss, and then they relax and get all friendly. Then you can muck about and do whatever you want.

I *love* mucking about, doing daft things and being a bit cheeky and making everyone laugh. Even the teachers. But the moment I set eyes on Miss Beckworth I knew none of us were going to be laughing. She might be new but she
10 certainly wasn't young. She had grey hair and grey eyes and a grey and white blouse and a grey skirt and laced-up shoes, with a laced-up expression on her face to match. When she spoke her teeth were quite big and stuck out a bit, but I put all thought of Bugs Bunny imitations right out of my head.

There are some teachers – just a few – who have YOU'D BETTER NOT MESS WITH ME! tattooed right across their foreheads. She frowned at me with this incredibly fierce forehead and said, 'Good morning. This isn't a very good start to the new school year.'

20 I stared at her. What was she on about? Why was she looking at her watch? I wasn't late. OK, the school bell had gone as I was crossing the playground, but you always get five minutes to get to your classroom.

'It's three minutes past nine,' Miss Beckworth announced. 'You're late.'

'No, I'm not,' I said. 'We're not counted late until it's five past.'

I didn't say it cheekily. I was perfectly polite. I was trying to be helpful, actually.

30 'You're *certainly* not off to a good start,' she goes. 'First you're late. And then you argue. My name's Miss Beckworth. What's your name?'

'Charlie, Miss Beckworth.' (See, *ever* so polite – because I could see I had to proceed d-e-l-i-c-a-t-e-l-y.)

'Your proper name?'

'Charlie Enright.'

'We don't seem to be connecting correctly, Miss Enright. Charlie isn't a proper name. It's a diminutive.'

40   She was trying to make *me* look pretty diminutive, obviously. I tried to act cool but I could feel my cheeks flushing. I have this very white skin that can be a real problem when I get mad or embarrassed. When you have a lot of long red hair and you get a red face too you start to look as if someone's put a match to you.

'Are you *Charles* Enright?'

I can't *stand* it when teachers go all sarcastic on you. A few of the kids tittered nervously. That posh prat Jamie laughed out loud. Typical. Angela and Lisa were looking all anguished, dying for me.

50   'I'm Charlotte Enright, Miss Beckworth. But I've never been called Charlotte at this school, only Charlie.'

'Well, I'm going to call you Charlotte, Charlotte. Because in my class we do things differently,' said Miss Beckworth.

You're telling me we do things differently. (Well, *I'm* telling *you*, but you know what I mean!) I wasn't allowed to go and sit with Angela. She'd promised to get to school ever so early to grab the best desk (and the one next to it for Lisa) and she'd done well. The desk right next to the window, with the hot pipe to toast my toes on when it got

60   chilly. But all in vain.

'No, don't go and sit down, Charlotte,' said Miss Beckworth. 'I was just about to explain to the whole class that while we get to know each other I'd like you all to sit in alphabetical order.'

We stared at her, gob-smacked.

Miss Beckworth spoke into the stunned silence, holding her register aloft.

'So, Anthony Andrews, you come and sit at this desk in the front, with Judith Ashwell beside you, and then –'

70 'But Judith's a girl, Miss!' Anthony protested in horror.

'Cleverly observed, Mr Andrews,' said Miss Beckworth. 'And kindly note, I call you Mr Andrews, not plain Mister. I would prefer you to call me Miss Beckworth. Not Miss.'

'But boys and girls never sit next to each other, Miss,' said Anthony. He's as thick as two short planks – *twenty*-two – but when Miss Beckworth's forehead wrinkled he rewound her little speech inside his empty head and took heed. 'Er, Miss Beckworth, Miss. I don't want to sit next to Judith!'

80 'Well, you needn't think I want to sit next to *you*,' said Judith. 'Oh Miss Beckworth, that's not fair!'

Miss Beckworth didn't care. 'I said things would be different in my class. I didn't say they would be fair,' she said. 'Now, get yourselves sorted out and stop fussing like a lot of silly babies. Who's next on the register? Laura Bernard, right, sit at the desk behind Anthony and Judith, and then...'

I hovered, signalling wild regret with my eyebrows to Angela, who'd got up half an hour early for nothing.

90 Angela's surname is Robinson, so obviously we wouldn't sit together. But Lisa is Lisa Field, right after me on the register, so it looked as if we were OK after all. It wasn't really fair on poor Angela if I sat next to Lisa two years running, but it couldn't be helped.

But it didn't work out like that.

'James Edwards, you sit at the desk at the back on the left,' said Miss Beckworth. 'With… ah, Charlotte Enright beside you.'

Jamie Edwards! The most revolting stuck-up boring boy in the whole class. The whole year, the whole school, the whole town, county, country, world, *universe*. I'd sooner squat in the stationery cupboard than sit next to him.

I thought quickly, my brain going whizz, flash, bang. Aha! Sudden inspiration!

'I'm afraid I can't see very well, Miss Beckworth,' I said, squinting up my eyes as if I badly needed glasses. 'If I sit at the back I won't be able to see the board. Sometimes I still have problems even at the front – so if Lisa Field can come and sit next to me again, then I'm used to her telling me stuff in case I can't read it for myself. Isn't that right, Lisa?'

This was all news to Lisa, but she nodded convincingly.

'Yes, Miss Beckworth, I always have to help Charlie,' said Lisa.

But Miss Beckworth wasn't fooled. 'I'm not convinced that you're short-sighted, Charlotte. Quick-witted, certainly. But until you bring me a note from your mother and another from your optician I'd like you to sit at the back beside James.'

That was it. I was doomed. There was no way out. I had to sit next to Jamie Edwards.

Illustrated by Polly Dunbar

The Demon Headmaster

GILLIAN CROSS

Dinah Glass is the new girl at a very strange school. It's her first day and she has a letter for the headmaster.

As she stepped through, Dinah glanced quickly round the room. It was the tidiest office she had ever seen. There were no papers, no files, no pictures on the walls. Just a large, empty-topped desk, a filing cabinet and a bookcase with a neat row of books.

She took it all in in one second and then forgot it as her eyes fell on the man standing by the window. He was tall and thin, dressed in an immaculate black suit. From his shoulders, a long, black teacher's gown hung in heavy folds, like wings, giving him the appearance of a huge crow. Only his head was startlingly white. Fair hair, almost as colourless as snow, lay round a face with paper-white skin and pallid lips. His eyes were hidden behind dark glasses, like two black holes in the middle of all the whiteness.

She cleared her throat. 'Hallo. I'm Dinah Glass and I –'

He raised a long, ivory-coloured hand. 'Please do not speak until you are asked. Idle chatter is an inefficient waste of energy.'

Unnervingly, he went on staring at her for a moment or two without saying anything else. Dinah wished she could see the eyes behind the dark lenses. With his eyes hidden, his expression was unreadable.

Finally, he waved a hand towards an upright chair, pulled round to face the desk. 'Sit down.' He sat down himself, facing her, and pulled a sheet of paper out of a drawer.

'Dinah Glass,' he said crisply, writing it down in neat, precise script. 'You are being fostered by Mrs. Hunter?'

Dinah nodded.

'Answer properly, please.'

'Yes, sir.'

'And why is she not here, to introduce you?'

'She couldn't come, but she's sent you a letter.'

Reaching across the desk, the Headmaster twitched it out of her hand and slit the envelope with a small steel paper knife. As he read the letter, Dinah settled herself more comfortably, expecting to be asked a string of questions.

But there were no questions. Instead, he pushed a sheet of paper across the desk towards her. 'This is a test,' he said. 'It is given to all new pupils.'

'Haven't you got a report on me?' Dinah said. 'From my other school?'

'No one else's reports are of any use to me,' said the Headmaster. 'Please be quiet and do the test.'

His voice was low, but somehow rather frightening. Dinah took a pen out of her pocket and looked down at the paper.

The questions were fairly hard. Mostly sums, with a bit of English thrown in and one or two brain-teasers. She knew that most children would have found them difficult to answer and she paused for a moment, working out where she was going to make her deliberate mistakes. Not too many. Just enough to avoid trouble.

Then she picked up the pen and began to write. As she scribbled, she could feel him watching her and every time she glanced up he was the same. Pale and motionless, with two black circles where his eyes should have been. She was so nervous that she stumbled once or twice, getting some of the answers right where she had meant to make mistakes. To keep the balance, she had to botch up all the last three questions. Not very good. It did not look as convincing as it should have done. Her hand trembled slightly as she passed the paper back across the table.

The Headmaster scanned it carefully for a moment, then looked up at her.

'You are an intelligent girl.'

Dinah's heart sank, but, with an effort, she kept her face calm, meeting the Headmaster's gaze steadily. At last, he
70 said, 'But you make too many mistakes. I wonder –' He chewed for a moment on his bottom lip. Then he shrugged. 'It doesn't matter. I dare say we shall find out all about you in due course.'

She looked down to the floor, trying not to seem too relieved, and waiting to be told which class she should go to. But the Headmaster did not seem in any hurry to get rid of her. He crumpled the test paper in his hand and dropped it into the rubbish bin. Then, slowly, he reached up a hand to take off his glasses.

80 Dinah found herself shivering. Ridiculously, she expected him to have pink eyes, because the rest of his face was so colourless. Or perhaps no eyes at all...

But his eyes were not pink. They were large and luminous, and a peculiar sea-green colour. She had never seen eyes like them before, and she found herself staring into them. Staring and staring.

'Funny you should be so tired,' he said, softly. 'So early in the morning.'

She opened her mouth to say that she was not tired,
90 but, to her surprise, she yawned instead.

'*So* tired,' crooned the Headmaster, his huge, extraordinary eyes fixed on her face. 'You can hardly move your arms and legs. You are so tired, so tired. You feel your head begin to nod and slowly, slowly your eyes are starting to close. *So* tired and sleepy.'

He's mad. Dinah thought muzzily. *The whole school's raving mad*. But she felt her eyes start to close, in spite of all she could do. She was drifting, drifting... All she could see was two pools, deep green like the sea, and she seemed
100 to sink into them as she drifted off and off...

59

Illustrated by Sholto Walker

kind of trouble!'

Tad could hardly speak for embarrassment. 'I'm sorry,' he muttered gruffly. 'Did I hurt you?'

The mother frowned, but the girl looked up at Tad with a sweet, angelic smile. Almost too perfect to be true.

'Don't fret. It didn't hurt at all. I can't feel much.'

Mrs Rinehimer sighed sympathetically and Tad shuffled his feet, feeling large and clumsy and uncouth. The girl was 80 smiling at him kindly enough, but she was the only one.

Then, suddenly, everything changed, with a great gasp of breath that started at the depot and came sighing down the tracks. The whole crowd turned to look right, and people began pushing and craning their necks. Tad turned too, but for a moment all he could make out was a forest of heads.

And then he saw the elephant.

It came ambling along the front of the crowd, between the main track and the siding. Its huge feet moved delicately over the rough stones and, from high on its neck, a miner 90 waved a nervous hand.

'Only twenty cents for an unforgettable experience!' said a voice like a trumpet. 'Take a ride on the elephant and feel, for yourself, man's domination of the greatest creature on earth!'

The elephant had almost reached Tad before he saw who was shouting. It was a short, flamboyant figure in a tall hat and a jacket lined with scarlet silk. He strode ahead, waving one arm dramatically and leading the elephant on a short length of frayed rope.

100 The elephant.

It passed close to Tad, not five paces away. Its side was like a wall of rock, grooved with a thousand interwoven wrinkles. A few hairs sprouted from the rock, like lichens on an ancient crag, and the ripe, grassy smell of elephant flesh filled the air.

Tad was mesmerized. If Mrs Bobb had hit him with a mallet, he wouldn't have noticed. If the girl with the crutches had burst into song, he wouldn't have heard.

110 He couldn't take his eyes from the great, slow body of the elephant.

The elephant stopped, twenty yards further up the line, to let the miner dismount. As it turned back towards Tad, he looked up into its face, at the small, remote eye, almost hidden in a cocoon of wrinkles.

'…most wondrously loyal and intelligent creatures!' the man in the tall hat bellowed, almost in Tad's ear. 'Capable of understanding a vast range of commands…'

Tad's eyes travelled over the humped head and down the long line of the trunk, to the massive legs. The nearest

120 foot was thicker than his whole body, with gnarled yellow toenails the size of his fist.

The great foot took one more step, and the man in the tall hat raised his voice, suddenly and sharply.

'But still I have not revealed the most amazing fact about Khush –'

He paused, as though to gather everyone's attention. It was a dramatic silence, and even Tad took his eyes off the elephant and

130 looked round, for a second.

And in that second, the elephant moved. The long, grey trunk snaked down – so close to Tad that it brushed his cheek – and looped itself round the girl with the crutches. Before anyone could react, it lifted her high into the air.

Illustrated by Peter Sutton

65

The Midnight Fox

Betsy Byars

Tom is staying with his aunt and uncle on their farm. He is bored and writes letters to his friend Petie. Then one day something happens...

I had just finished writing a letter and was waiting for a minute to see if I would think of anything to add when I looked up and saw the black fox.

I did not believe it for a minute. It was like my eyes were playing a trick or something, because I was just sort of staring across this field, thinking about my letter, and then in the distance, where the grass was very green, I saw a fox leaping over the crest of the field. The grass moved and the fox sprang towards the movement, and then, seeing that it was just the wind that had caused the grass to move, she ran straight for the grove of trees where I was sitting.

It was so great that I wanted it to start over again, like you can turn movie film back and see yourself repeat some fine thing you have done, and I wanted to see the fox leaping over the grass again. In all my life I have never been so excited.

I did not move at all, but I could hear the paper in my hand shaking, and my heart seemed to have moved up in my body and got stuck in my throat.

The fox came straight towards the grove of trees. She wasn't afraid, and I knew she had not seen me against the tree. I stayed absolutely still even though I felt like jumping up and screaming, 'Aunt Millie! Uncle Fred! Come see this. It's a fox, a *fox*!'

Her steps as she crossed the field were lighter and quicker than a cat's. As she came closer I could see that her black fur was tipped with white. It was as if it were midnight and the moon were shining on her fur, frosting it. The wind parted her fur as it changed directions. Suddenly she stopped. She was ten feet away now, and with the changing

66

of the wind she got my scent. She looked right at me.

I did not move for a moment and neither did she. Her head was cocked to one side, her tail curled up, her front left foot raised. In all my life I never saw anything like that fox standing there with her pale green golden eyes on me and this great black fur being blown by the wind.

Suddenly her nose quivered. It was such a slight movement I almost didn't see it, and then her mouth opened and I could see the pink tip of her tongue. She turned. She still was not afraid, but with a bound that was lighter than the wind – it was as if she was being blown away over the field – she was gone.

Still I didn't move. I couldn't. I couldn't believe that I had really seen the fox.

I had seen foxes before in zoos, but I was always in such a great hurry to get on to the good stuff that I was saying stupid things like, 'I want to see the go-rilllllllas,' and not once had I ever really looked at a fox. Still, I could never remember seeing a black fox, not even in a zoo.

Also, there was a great deal of difference between seeing an animal in the zoo in front of painted fake rocks and trees and seeing one natural and free in the woods. It was like seeing a kite on the floor and then, later, seeing one up in the sky where it was supposed to be, pulling at the wind.

I started to pick up my pencil and write as quickly as I could, 'P.S. Today I saw a black fox.' But I didn't. This was the most exciting thing that had happened to me, and 'P.S. Today I saw a black fox' made it nothing. 'So what else is happening?' Petie Burkis would probably write back. I folded my letter, put it in an envelope, and sat there.

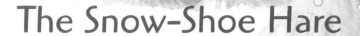

The Snow-Shoe Hare

The Snow-Shoe Hare
Is his own sudden blizzard.

Or he comes, limping after the snowstorm,
A big, lost, left-behind snowflake
Crippled with bandages.

White, he is looking for a great whiteness
To hide in.
But the starry night is on his track –

His own dogged shadow
Panics him to right, and to left, and backwards,
        and forwards –
Till he skids skittering
Out over the blue ice, meeting the Moon.

He stretches, craning slender
Listening
For the Fox's icicles and the White Owl's slow cloud.

In his popping eyes
The whole crowded heaven struggles softly.

Glassy mountains, breathless, brittle forests
Are frosty aerials
Balanced in his ears.

And his nose bobs wilder
And his hot red heart thuds harder

Tethered so tightly
To his crouching shadow.

TED HUGHES

Illustrated by Nicolette Green

Mooses

The goofy Moose, the walking house-frame,
Is lost
In the forest. He bumps, he blunders, he stands.

With massy bony thoughts sticking out near his ears –
Reaching out palm upwards, to catch whatever might be
    falling from heaven –
He tries to think,
Leaning their huge weight
On the lectern of his front legs.

He can't find the world!
Where did it go? What does a world look like?
The Moose
Crashes on, and crashes into a lake, and stares at the
    mountain, and cries
"Where do I belong? This is no place!"

He turns and drags half the lake out after him
And charges the cackling underbrush –

He meets another Moose.
He stares, he thinks "It's only a mirror!"

"Where is the world?" he groans, "O my lost world!
And why am I so ugly?
And why am I so far away from my feet?"

He weeps.
Hopeless drops drip from his droopy lips.

The other Moose just stands there doing the same.

Two dopes of the deep woods.

TED HUGHES

Illustrated by Nicolette Green

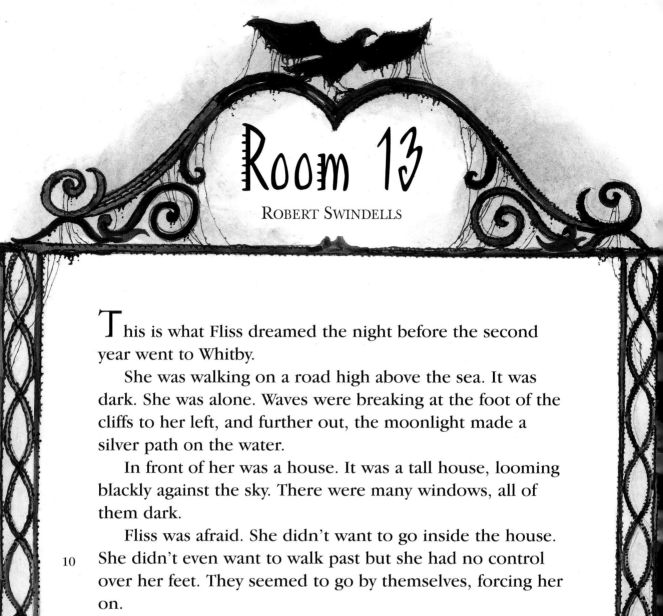

Room 13

ROBERT SWINDELLS

This is what Fliss dreamed the night before the second year went to Whitby.

She was walking on a road high above the sea. It was dark. She was alone. Waves were breaking at the foot of the cliffs to her left, and further out, the moonlight made a silver path on the water.

In front of her was a house. It was a tall house, looming blackly against the sky. There were many windows, all of them dark.

Fliss was afraid. She didn't want to go inside the house. She didn't even want to walk past but she had no control over her feet. They seemed to go by themselves, forcing her on.

She came to a gate. It was made of iron, worked into curly patterns. Near the top was a bit that was supposed to be a bird in flight – a seagull perhaps – but the gate had been painted black, and the paint had run and hardened into little stalactites along the bird's wings, making it look like a bat.

The gate opened by itself, and as she went through Fliss heard a voice that whispered, 'The Gate of Fate.' She was drawn along a short pathway and up some stone steps to the front door, which also opened by itself. 'The Keep of Sleep,' whispered the voice.

The door closed silently behind her. Moonlight shone coldly through a stained-glass panel into a gloomy hallway. At the far end were stairs that went up into blackness. She didn't want to climb that stairway but her feet drew her along the hallway and up.

30   She came to a landing with doors. The stairs took a turn and went on up. As Fliss climbed, it grew colder. There was another landing, more doors and another turn in the stair. Upward to a third landing, then a fourth, and then there were no more stairs. She was at the top of the house. There were four doors, each with a number. 10. 11. 12. 13. As she read the numbers, door thirteen swung inward with a squeal. 'No!' she whispered, but it was no use. Her feet carried her over the threshold and the voice hissed, 'The Room of Doom.'

40   In the room was a table. On the table stood a long, pale box. Fliss thought she knew what it was. It filled her with horror, and she whimpered helplessly as her feet drew her towards it. When she was close she saw a shape in the box and there was a smell like damp earth. When she was very close the voice whispered, 'The Bed of Dread,' and then the shape sat up and reached out for her and she screamed. Her screams woke her and she lay damp and trembling in her bed.

50   Her mother came and switched on the light and looked down at her. 'What is it Felicity? I thought I heard you scream.'

Fliss nodded. 'I had a dream, Mum. A nightmare.'

'Poor Fliss.' Her mother sat down on the bed and stroked her hair. 'It's all the excitement, I expect – thinking about going away tomorrow.' She smiled. 'Try to go back to sleep, dear. You've a long day ahead of you.'

Fliss clutched her mother's arm. 'I don't want to go, Mum.'

60   'What?'

'I don't want to go. I want to drop out of the trip.'

'But why – not just because of a silly dream, surely?'

'Well, yes. I suppose so, Mum. It was about Whitby, I think. A house by the sea.'

'A house?'

'Yes.' She shivered, remembering. 'I was in this house and something horrible was after me. Can I drop out, Mum?'

Her mother sighed. 'I suppose you could, Felicity, if
70   you're as upset as all that. I could ring Mrs Evans first thing, tell her not to expect you, but you might feel differently in the morning.' She smiled. 'Daylight makes us forget our dreams, or else they seem funny – even the scary ones. Let's decide in the morning, eh?'

Fliss smiled wanly. 'OK.' She knew she wouldn't forget her dream, and that it would never seem funny. But it was all right. She was in control of her feet (she wiggled them under the covers to make sure), and they weren't going to take her anywhere she didn't want to go.

Illustrated by Victor G. Ambrus

Marianne Dreams

CATHERINE STORR

Marianne dreamed. She was in a great open stretch of country, flat like a prairie, covered, as far as she could see, with the long dry grass in which she was standing more than knee deep. There were no roads, no paths, no hills and no valleys. Only the prairie stretched before her on all sides till it met the grey encircling sky. Here and there it was dotted with great stones or rocks, which rose just above the level of the tall grass, like heads peering from all directions.

Marianne stood and looked. There seemed to be nothing to do and nowhere to go. Wherever she looked she saw nothing but grass and stones and sky, the same on every side of her. Yet something, a nagging uneasiness which she could not account for, drove her to start walking; and because at one point on the skyline she thought she could see something like a faint trickle of smoke, she walked towards that.

The ground under her feet was rutted and uneven, and the grass harsh and prickling. She could not move fast, and it seemed that she had walked a long way before she saw that she had been right about the faint line in the sky. It was a wavering stream of smoke, rising in the windless air from the chimney of a house.

It was a curious looking house, with leaning walls, its windows and door blank and shut. It rose unexpectedly straight from the prairie: a low uneven fence separated its small plot from the surrounding ground, though the coarse grass was the same within and without. There were some large pale yellow flowers about, which Marianne could not recognize, growing a foot or two high; they seemed to be as much outside the fence as in, and certainly did not constitute a garden. Nothing moved except the thread of smoke rising from the chimney. In all that vast expanse nothing else moved.

There was a gate in the fence. Marianne pushed it open and walked up the path to the door. She did not much like the look of the house, with its blank staring windows and its bare front door, but she liked the prairie even less. 'I must get in,' said Marianne aloud in her dream. 'I've got to get in.'

40 There was no knocker and there was no bell. Marianne knocked with her knuckles, but it was a disappointing little noise and she was not surprised that no one answered. She looked around for a stone to beat on the door but the only stones were the great grey boulders outside the fence. As she stood, considering what to do, she heard the distant sound of wind. Across the prairie it blew towards her, and in its path the grass whistled and rustled, dry stalk on dry stalk, and bent, so that she could see the path of the wind as it approached her. Then it was all around her, and everything that had been so still before became alive with 50 movement. The grass writhed and tore at its roots, the pale flowers beat against their stems, the thin thread of smoke was blown out like a candle flame, and disappeared into the dark sky. The wind whistled round the house and was gone, leaving Marianne deaf for a moment, and suddenly chilled.

'I'm frightened here,' she said. 'I've got to get away from the grass and the stones and the wind. I've got to get into the house.' No voice spoke in reply to her words, and there was no signal from the silent house; but she knew the answer as if she had heard it.

60 'I could get in,' Marianne thought, 'if there was a person inside the house. There has got to be a person. I can't get in unless there is somebody there.'

'Why isn't there someone in the house?' she cried to the empty world around her.

'Put someone there,' the silent answer said.

'How can I?' Marianne protested. 'How can I put someone in the house? I can't get in myself! And I've got to get in!'

'I've got to get in!' she heard herself say, and the words woke her up. With difficulty she struggled back to realize 70 that the house and prairie were gone: she was lying in bed, and the memory of the six weeks more to be spent there was lying in wait for her, to weigh down her spirits as soon as she was sufficiently awake to remember.

Illustrated by Bee Willey

Junior School Sports

Sports Day's over.
It's four o'clock.
The mats have all been stacked away,
the benches and the chairs
all cleared away,
the Mums and Dads and little kids
have all gone home for tea.

There's just a handful of us
Fourth Years stayed behind
to help collect up all the bean-bags,
hoops and balls
and batons from the relay.

Sports Day's over.
But what a great day!
I won the rounders ball,
a throw of 40 metres – beat the record!
The one thing, maybe the only thing,
I'm *really* good at.
This has been the best day of my life.

The last week
of the last term
of the Fourth Year.
Tomorrow is the very last day

and I don't want today to end
I want to stretch this afternoon out
like a rubber band, I want
this afternoon to last
for ever.

Daft!
I know it can't.
I've seen all year how
everything's too small,
how I've outgrown it all –

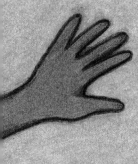

the chairs too low,
the corridors too narrow,
the climbing ropes too easy,
the playground and the hall too cramped.

Sports Day's over
and that's that.
At my feet
the last wire crate of rounders balls,
the last thing
waiting to be put away.

Next year
It'll all be different.
I'll be a First Year then,
just a little kid again.
I won't be best at anything next year!

Go on, girl –
one last throw?

A short run –
                        back foot
                        front foot – **Hurl!**

Watch it soar –
20 – 30 – 40 metres … Go on! Go on!
50 – 60 … Don't stop! Don't ever stop!
See the white ball
arc across the clear blue sky –

'Julie! I'm surprised at you!
This isn't the time to
mess about.
Go and get it
     – now!'

'Yes, Miss. Sorry, Miss.
Don't worry, Miss,
It won't happen again –'

MICK GOWAR

Illustrated by Nick Sharratt

The Bully Asleep

One afternoon, when grassy
Scents through the classroom crept,
Bill Craddock laid his head
Down on his desk, and slept.

The children came round him:
Jimmy, Roger and Jane;
They lifted his head timidly
And let it sink again.

'Look, he's gone sound asleep, Miss,'
Said Jimmy Adair;
'He stays up all the night, you see;
His mother doesn't care.'

'Stand away from him children.'
Miss Andrews stooped to see.
'Yes, he's asleep; go on
With your writing, and let him be.'

'Now's a good chance!' whispered Jimmy;
And he snatched Bill's pen and hid it.
'Kick him under the desk, hard;
He won't know who did it.'

'Fill all his pockets with rubbish –
Paper, apple-cores, chalk.'
So they plotted, while Jane
Sat wide-eyed at their talk.

Not caring, not hearing,
Bill Craddock he slept on;
Lips parted, eyes closed –
Their cruelty gone.

'Stick him with pins!' muttered Roger.
'Ink down his neck!' said Jim.
But Jane, tearful and foolish,
Wanted to comfort him.

Illustrated by Alan Marks

JOHN WALSH

The Hate

We began each morning with hymns,
'Lots of wind' our teacher called
as she wrestled a melody
from the ancient hall piano.

Then we sat and gazed at the front
while the football team results were read
and Donald was led in, held by the arm,
a look of alarm on his face.
I didn't know what he'd done,
perhaps he'd stolen or two-fingered
once too often. It must have been serious,
in the eyes of God, in the eyes of
our Headmistress.

Her philosophy seemed to be
that boys' backsides were meant to be whacked
but Donald struggled and lay on the floor
and flapped like a fish out of water.
Even the toughies were terrified
as the slipper rose and fell
a total of eighteen times till it stopped
and Donald stayed locked to the floor.

The piano was open but no one played
as we filed out silent and found our maths.
It stayed on our minds for much of the day
but Donald wouldn't say what he'd done,
just shook his head and said nothing.

Our teacher said Donald would be forgiven,
start once again and clean the slate;
but I glimpsed him next day in prayers,
a dreadful look on his face, and I knew
it would take more than Jesus
to wipe away the hate.

BRIAN MOSES

Illustrated by Alan Marks

Acknowledgements

Cider with Rosie from *Cider with Rosie* by Laurie Lee, published by The Hogarth Press and reproduced with permission of Random House UK Ltd

Matilda from *Matilda* by Roald Dahl (Jonathan Cape). Reproduced with permission of David Higham Associates

Macbeth from *Shakespeare, The Animated Tales* by Leon Garfield, published by William Heinemann (a division of Egmont Children's Books Ltd)

Rikki-Tikki-Tavi from *The Jungle Book* by Rudyard Kipling. Reproduced with kind permission of AP Watt Ltd, on behalf of the National Trust for Places of Historic Interest or Natural Beauty

A Tutor Who Tooted the Flute by Carolyn Wells, © Carolyn Wells

There Was an Old Man in a Trunk by Ogden Nash from *The Collected Poems of Ogden Nash*. Reproduced with permission of AP Watt Ltd

Black Dot from *All Change* (OUP 1993) by Libby Houston, by kind permission of the author

Swap? Sell? Small Ads Sell Fast by Trevor Millum, © Trevor Millum, first published in *Warning, Too Much Schooling Can Damage Your Health* (Thomas Nelson)

Christmas Thank Yous from *Swings and Roundabouts* by Mick Gowar (HarperCollins). Reproduced with permission of HarperCollins Publishers Ltd

Tom's Midnight Garden by Philippa Pearce (OUP). Reproduced with permission of Laura Cecil Literary Agent, on behalf of the author

The Ghost of Thomas Kempe by Penelope Lively, published by William Heinemann (a division of Egmont Children's Books Ltd)

The Listeners by Walter de la Mare, reproduced with permission of the Literary Trustees of Walter de la Mare, and the Society of Authors as their representative

Silver by Walter de la Mare from *The Complete Poems of Walter de la Mare*, 1969. Reproduced with permission of the Literary Trustees of Walter de la Mare, and the Society of Authors as their representative

The Silver Sword by Ian Serraillier, published by Heinemann, reproduced with permission of Random House, UK Ltd

The War of the Worlds by HG Wells, published by William Heinemann Ltd and reproduced with kind permission of AP Watt Ltd, on behalf of the literary executors of the estate of HG Wells

The Lottie Project by Jacqueline Wilson, © 1997 Jacqueline Wilson. Extracted from *The Lottie Project* published by Doubleday, a division of Transworld Publishers Ltd. All rights reserved.

The Demon Headmaster by Gillian Cross (OUP), reproduced with permission of Oxford University Press

A Haiku Yearbook by Anthony Thwaite, from *Poems 1953-1988* (1989), © the author, Anthony Thwaite

The Great Elephant Chase by Gillian Cross (OUP), reproduced by kind permission of Oxford University Press

The Midnight Fox by Betsy Byars (Faber and Faber), reproduced by permission of Faber and Faber

The Snow-Shoe Hare from *Under the North Star* by Ted Hughes (Faber and Faber), reproduced by permission of Faber and Faber

Mooses from *Under the North Star* by Ted Hughes (Faber and Faber), reproduced by permission of Faber and Faber

Room 13 by Robert Swindells, © 1989 Robert Swindells. Extracted from *Room 13* published by Yearling, a division of Transworld Publishers Ltd. All rights reserved.

Marianne Dreams by Catherine Storr (Faber and Faber), reproduced with permission of Faber and Faber Ltd

Junior School Sports by Mick Gowar, from *Third Time Unlucky* (Viking Kestrel, 1988) © Mick Gowar 1988

The Bully Asleep by John Walsh, from *Poets in Hand* (Puffin, 1985) © Patrick Walsh

The Hate by Brian Moses, © the author, Brian Moses

Every effort has been made to trace copyright holders but we would be glad to rectify any omissions at the next reprint